TONE
DEVELOPMENT

For

FLUTE

By

EMIL ECK

FOREWORD

The attainment of a clear, radiant and beautiful tone is probably the most cherished aim of every flute student. It is of paramount importance and its achievement, therefore, a point both valuable and necessary.

As with any other wind instrument, tone production is the result of intensive slow and even legato playing and attained through regular and patient practice.

With this object in mind, the author has prepared this volume of studies; short, melodious and rhythmically as varied as possible considering the grade of the student.

SEQUENCE

Starting with extremely easy exercises, the material has been staggered slowly with regard to technical difficulty and rhythmical pattern.

To insure slowness in playing, sixteenth notes are not introduced with the exception of some dotted eighths and sixteenths in the last pages.

On page thirty is a facsimile of a scale and chord study which has been found valuable both for tone and technical developement and should be followed through all keys.

SUGGESTIONS

Diaphragmatic breathing should be stressed from the start. Play evenly with a normal breath and not too much contraction of the diaphragm resulting in a steady, slight pressure. This necessitates a steady, somewhat firm lip control with the lip opening small and flexible. Support this with a gentle but firm lower jaw control. The rest of the face, especially the throat should be relaxed. To insure flexibility of the jaw, the flute should never be pressed hard against it.

Start a tone with the tongue, like ejecting a particle of food from the opening of the lips.

This phase will be discussed in greater detail in a subsequent volume on tongueing.

The Author

E.L.-796

TONE DEVELOPMENT FOR FLUTE

4

DUET

E.L.-796

E.L.-796

Slow - Start soft, increase as much as possible.

E.L.-796   cresc. . . . . .ff

11

Slow, heavy

DUET

In a playful mood.

TRIPLETS

E.L.-796

DUET

DUET

Allegretto- Slow 2

Not Fast

E. L.-796

With full tone.

rall.   a tempo

rall.   a tempo

This scale exercies should if possible be performed four measures to one breath. In order to acquire this period, sustain a single note for four measures as outlined in the first line.

Two octaves up and down.

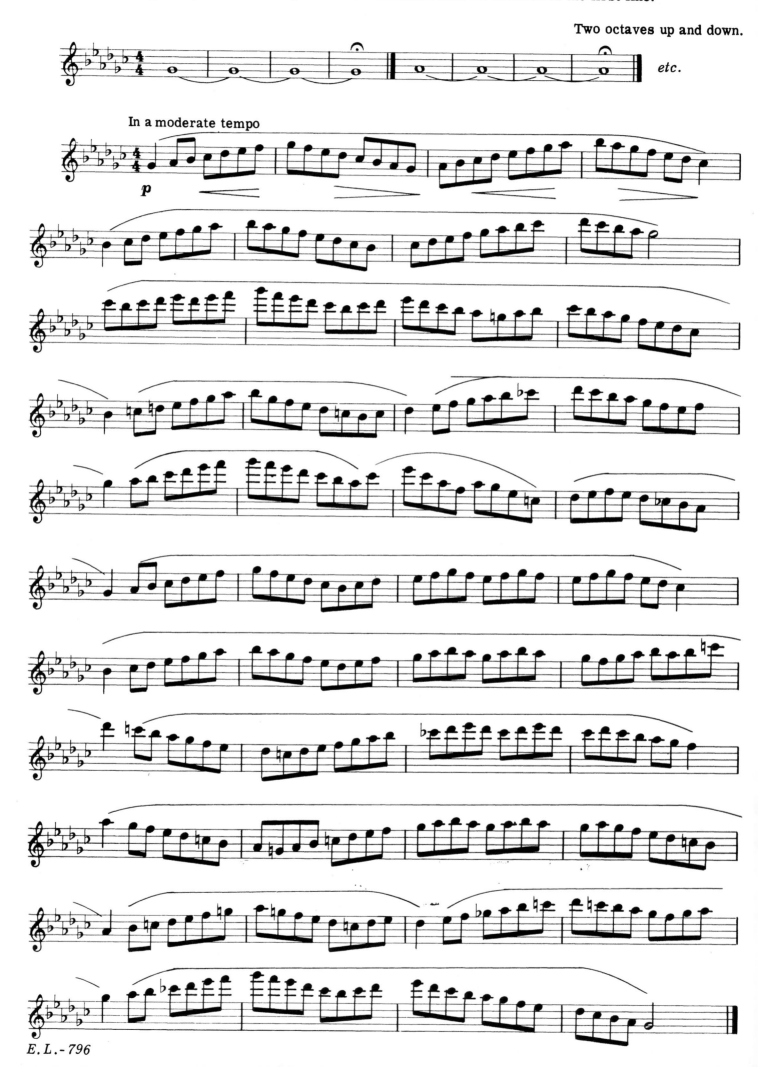

In a moderate tempo

Moderato, simple and graceful

Moderately fast – in 2

A FACSIMILE OF A SCALE AND SHORD STUDY
To be practiced through all Major and Minor Keys.

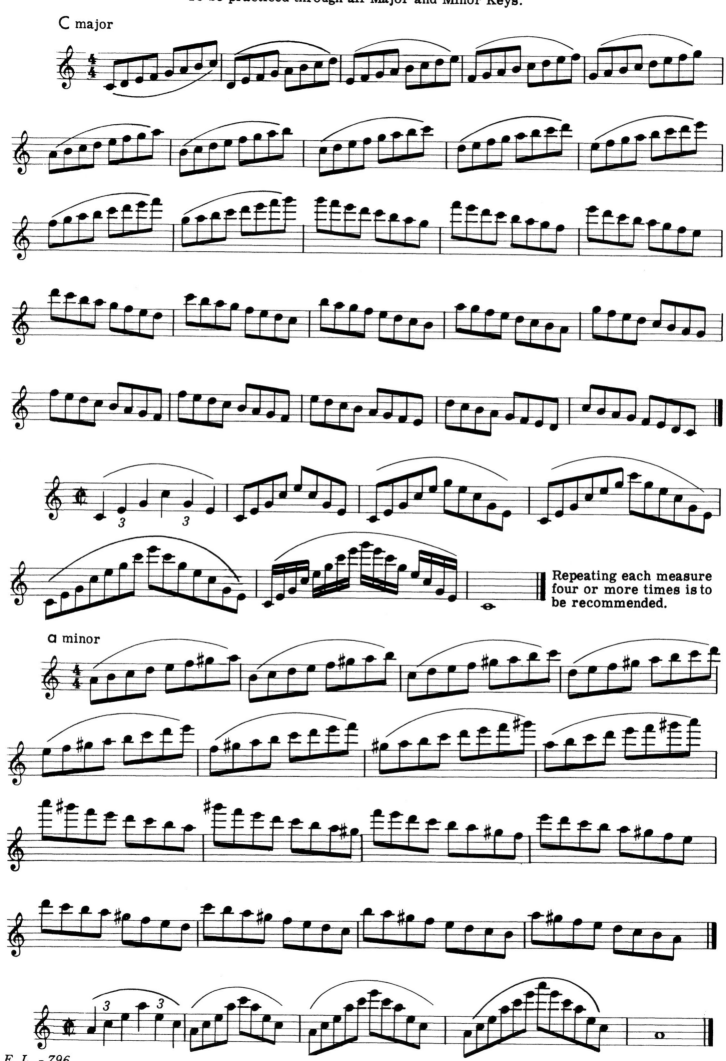

Repeating each measure
four or more times is to
be recommended.

E.L.-796

* C minor should if possible be practiced to high c.